ORSON CART

AND THE

SHIPWRECK SHARKS

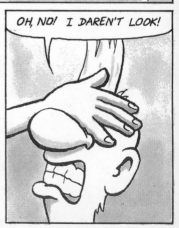

DOLPHINS ARE VERY INTELLIGENT CREATURES, BUT WE DON'T KNOW VERY MUCH ABOUT THEM. I'M TRYING TO FIND A WAY TO TALK THEIR LANGUAGE. THAT'S WHAT THIS LAB IS FOR.

BLIMEY! THEY TALK?

IN SQUEAKS AND CLICKS MOSTLY, BUT I'VE LEARNED ONE OR TWO BITS OF IT. FOR EXAMPLE, HIS NAME IS *SKREE-KT-KT -EEE-AWK!*

OUCH! THAT HURTS!

WELL, I JUST CALL HIM DODGER.

BACK AT THE LAB—

PROF! PROF! WE GOT ATTACKED BY A SHARK!

ARE YOU ALL RIGHT?

YES, BUT...

GOOD! BUT DON'T GO OFF BY YOURSELVES AGAIN THEN. SHARKS ARE DANGEROUS, YOU KNOW.

YES, BUT YOU WON'T BELIEVE WHAT ELSE WE SAW!

PROBABLY NOT, BUT I DON'T HAVE TIME TO LISTEN RIGHT NOW. I'M WORKING ON MY DOLPHIN TRANSLATOR.

GO AND PLAY WITH THE COMPUTER OR SOMETHING.

BUT, PROF!...

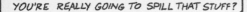

YOU'RE REALLY GOING TO SPILL THAT STUFF?

JUST SO YOU CAN MAKE MONEY?

NOT ME! NO! I'M NOT THAT STUPID! I WILL BE SAFE ON BOARD SHIP WHEN MY FRIENDS THE SHARKS COME TO OPEN THE DRUMS. I TRAINED THEM TO OPEN BIG TINS OF FISH — BUT THEY DON'T KNOW THE DIFFERENCE!

THIS TIME IT'S MORE IMPORTANT! YOU TWO COULD SEND ME TO PRISON!

DO YOU KNOW WHAT'S ON THOSE SATELLITE PICTURES? EVIDENCE! THEY SHOW THAT MOST OF THE POLLUTION ACCIDENTS HAPPEN CLOSE TO MY SHIP — SOMETIMES THE POLLUTION COMES FROM MY SHIP! I KNEW I HAD TO FIND THAT SATELLITE FIRST!

I KNEW ROUGHLY WHERE IT FELL, SO I HAD MY SHARKS SINK THIS SHIP NEARBY. THE POLLUTION WOULD HAVE KEPT EVERYONE ELSE AWAY — BUT THE DRUMS DIDN'T BREAK! THEN YOU FOUND IT FIRST!

WE DIDN'T FIND IT! THE DOLPHINS DID!

WELL, IT DOESN'T MATTER. THEY'LL ALL DIE TOO.

OH YES. BEFORE I FORGET. GIVE ME THOSE MICROPHONES. I DON'T WANT THE PROFESSOR HEARING YOUR CRIES FOR HELP!

THANK YOU.

ORSON! WHAT ARE YOU DOING OUT THERE? WHERE'S THE REST OF YOU?

KNOCK! KNOCK!

ORSON? HELLO? CAN YOU HEAR ME?

YOU CAN? BUT I CAN'T HEAR YOU. WHAT'S GOING ON?

WILL THE SHARKS UNLEASH THE LETHAL POISON?

WILL THE PROF. GUESS WHAT ORSON IS SAYING?

OR WILL THIS GUESSING GAME GO ON FOREVER?

FIND OUT IN—

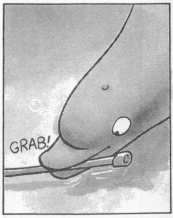

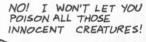

MEANWHILE —

WE'RE WINNING! THE SHARKS ARE GIVING UP!

WE'RE SAFE!